My Son is Sick

The New East Enders Series

Written by Marta Paluch

Illustrated by Mary Pierce

My Son is Sick

Published in 2014 by Gatehouse Media Limited

ISBN: 978-1-84231-089-2

British Library Cataloguing-in-Publication Data:
A catalogue record for this book is available from the British Library

Authors' Note

In 2003 the ESOL Outreach team at Tower Hamlets College gained funding from the East London ESOL Pathfinder to produce a pack of teaching materials relevant to the context of Outreach ESOL classes. Tower Hamlets College was the lead partner for the East London ESOL Pathfinder.

The resulting pack of materials included 6 easy reading booklets for beginning ESOL learners. The reading booklets proved popular and it was suggested that we should try to get them published. We approached Avantibooks who agreed to publish them as a series entitled *The New Eastenders*, but those books are now out of print.

We are delighted that they have now been given a new lease of life by Gatehouse Books as *The New East Enders Series* for a new generation of ESOL learners. We have added a seventh title to the series, called *My Mother-in-Law*, and a useful set of tutor resources and student worksheets. We hope you enjoy using them.

Marta Paluch & Mary Pierce

Jahangir wakes up in the morning.
He's got a headache and a sore throat.

Amina takes his temperature.

It's 38 degrees.

Amina's mother-in-law says,
"Make a hot lemon drink."

Amina's father-in-law says,
"Vicks is good."

Amina's husband says,
"Go to the doctor."

Amina phones the doctor.

She makes an appointment.

She phones the school.

"I'm sorry, Jahangir can't come today," she says.

"He is sick."

Amina takes Jahangir to the doctor.
She sits in the waiting room.
Jahangir is tired.

The doctor examines Jahangir.
"It's not serious," she says.
"Give him hot lemon drinks."

Amina goes home with Jahangir.

She makes a hot lemon drink.
Jahangir goes to bed.

Today Amina has an English lesson.
She phones the centre.
"I'm sorry, I can't come," she says.
"My son is sick."

The next day Jahangir is better.
He goes to school.

Amina goes to her English lesson.

If you have enjoyed this book, why not try one of these other titles from *The New East Enders Series:*

A New Home
Fadumo Goes Shopping
From Here to There
Good Neighbours
My Mother-in-Law
Rima's Day

A comprehensive set of tutor resources is available to support this series of readers:

The New East Enders Series
Tutor Resources CD-ROM

ISBN: 978-1-84231-094-6

Gatehouse Books®

Gatehouse Books are written for older teenagers and adults who are developing their basic reading and writing or English language skills.

The format of our books is clear and uncluttered.
The language is familiar and the text is often line-broken, so that each line ends at a natural pause.

Gatehouse Books are widely used within Adult Basic Education throughout the English speaking world. They are also a valuable resource within the Prison Education Service and Probation Services, Social Services and secondary schools - both in basic skills and ESOL teaching.

Catalogue available

Gatehouse Media Limited
PO Box 965
Warrington
WA4 9DE

Tel/Fax: 01925 267778
E-mail: info@gatehousebooks.com
Website: www.gatehousebooks.com